Th[e]
Lost [Sheep]

GW01043830

Parables of Je[sus]
Words by Meryl Doney
Pictures by Graham Round

When Jesus wanted to teach his friends
something important he used to say:
'I'll tell you a story. Listen very hard
and you will understand it.'
The Lost Sheep is one of the
stories Jesus told.

Little Lions

One day Jesus' friends asked him:
'Who does God love most?'
'My father loves everyone,' said Jesus. He pointed to a little child.
'Children are not big and strong. They trust their parents to look after them. My father wants people to trust him and love him just like that. He will look after them.'
'What if they go away from God, and don't love him?' asked one of Jesus' friends.
So Jesus told this story.

Once upon a time, there was a shepherd who had a hundred sheep.

He looked after them. He found them grass to eat and water to drink.

At night he led them safely home to their sheep-pen.

The shepherd counted them as they went in through the gate.

One night he counted and there were only ninety-nine sheep.

One sheep was lost. The shepherd was very worried.

He set off straight away to look for the sheep.

He took with him his shepherd's stick and a bag of food.

He called to the sheep as he walked. Soon it was dark.

But still the shepherd searched among the rocks and prickly bushes.

Suddenly, the shepherd heard a feeble bleat. It was his sheep crying.

He ran towards the sound.

There was his sheep, caught in the bushes!

He used his shepherd's stick to get her out. Then he took her in his arms.

He carried her back to the sheep-pen on his shoulders.

The ninety-nine sheep were safe inside, waiting for him.

Gently the shepherd put his lost sheep down with the others.

She was so glad to be back home. She skipped and jumped for joy.

The shepherd was glad, too. He hurried to tell all his friends.

'I have found my lost sheep. I am going to have a party,' he said.

Some brought pipes and drums to make music.
Others sang and danced.

It was a wonderful party.

Everyone was glad the sheep had been found.

. . . and she was glad to be safe home again, too.

'My father is like that shepherd,' said Jesus.
'He knows us all by name. If one of us goes away
from him, he will come to look for us, because he
loves us. When he brings us back, he is as glad as
the shepherd in my story.'

You can find this story in your Bible:
Matthew 18:10-14